Irish Songs

Wise Publications
London/New York/Paris/Sydney/
Copenhagen/Madrid

Exclusive Distributors:
Music Sales Limited
8/9 Frith Street, London W1V 5TZ, England.
Music Sales Pty Limited
120 Rothschild Avenue, Rosebery, NSW 2018, Australia.

Order No. AM952567
ISBN 0-7119-7210-9
This book © Copyright 1998 by Wise Publications

Compiled by Peter Evans
Music arranged by Stephen Duro
Music processed by Allegro Reproductions
Cover photograph courtesy Images Colour Library

Printed in the United Kingdom by
Halstan & Co Limited, Amersham, Buckinghamshire.

Your Guarantee of Quality
As publishers, we strive to produce every book to the highest commercial standards.

The music has been freshly engraved and the book has been carefully designed to minimise
awkward page turns and to make playing from it a real pleasure.

Particular care has been given to specifying acid-free, neutral-sized paper made from pulps
which have not been elemental chlorine bleached. This pulp is from farmed sustainable forests
and was produced with special regard for the environment.

Throughout, the printing and binding have been planned to ensure a sturdy, attractive publication
which should give years of enjoyment.

If your copy fails to meet our high standards, please inform us and we will gladly replace it.

Music Sales' complete catalogue describes thousands of titles and is available in full colour sections
by subject, direct from Music Sales Limited. Please state your areas of interest
and send a cheque/postal order for £1.50 for postage to:
Music Sales Limited, Newmarket Road, Bury St. Edmunds, Suffolk IP33 3YB.

Visit the Internet Music Shop at
http://www.musicsales.co.uk

A Bunch Of Thyme

Traditional

Moderately

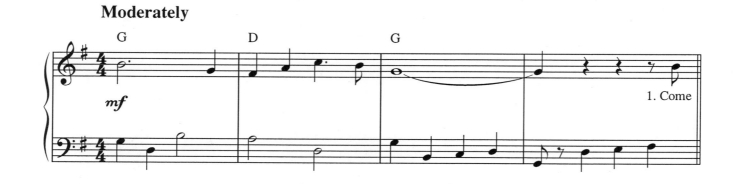

mf

1. Come

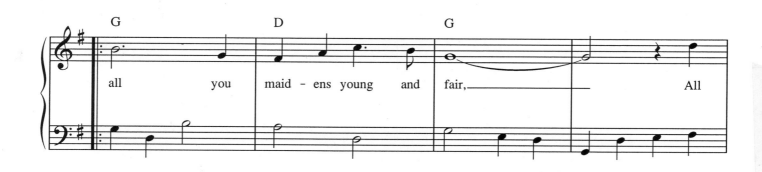

all you maid - ens young and fair,_____ All

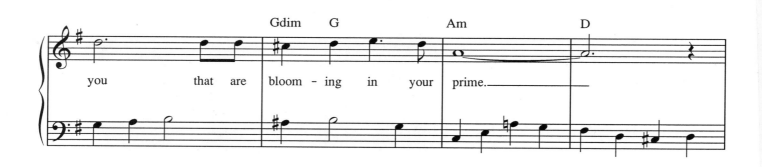

you that are bloom - ing in your prime._____

Al - ways be - ware_____ And keep your gar - den

fair,   Let   no   man   steal   a - way   your

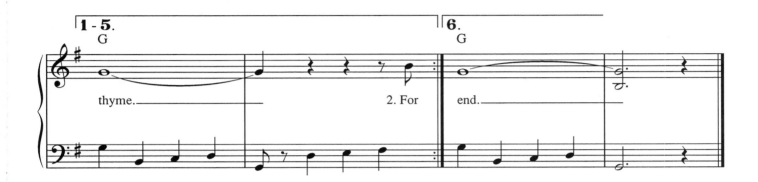

thyme.   2. For   end.

Verse 2:

For thyme it is a precious thing
And thyme brings all things to my mind.
Thyme, with all its labours
Along with all its joys
Thyme brings all things to my mind.

Verse 3:

Once she had a bunch of thyme,
She thought it would never decay,
Then came a lusty sailor
Who chanced to pass her way.
He stole her bunch of thyme away.

Verse 4:

The sailor gave to her a rose,
A rose that never would decay,
He gave it to her
To keep her reminded
Of when he stole her thyme away.

Verse 5:
Repeat Verse 1

Verse 6:

For thyme it is a precious thing
And thyme brings all things to my mind.
Thyme, with all its labours
Along with all its joys
Thyme brings all things to an end.

Back In Old Ireland

Words by Eddie Gillanders & Pat Michael
Music by Dennis Cummings & Douglas Cummings

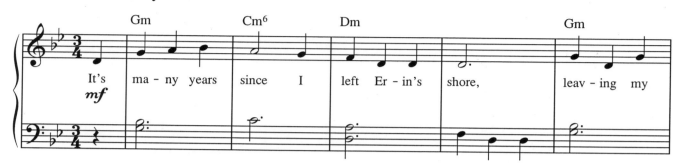

Cockles And Mussels

Traditional

Not too slow

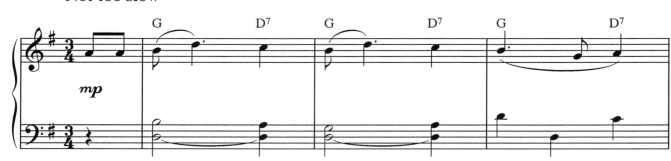

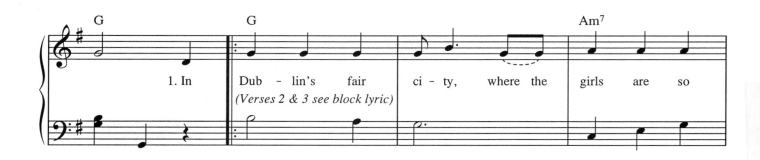

1. In Dub - lin's fair ci - ty, where the girls are so
(Verses 2 & 3 see block lyric)

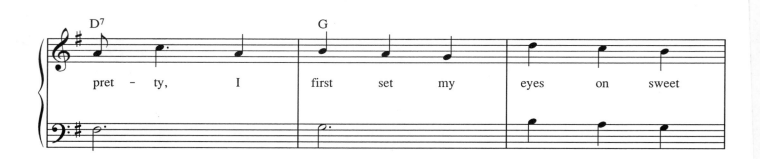

pret - ty, I first set my eyes on sweet

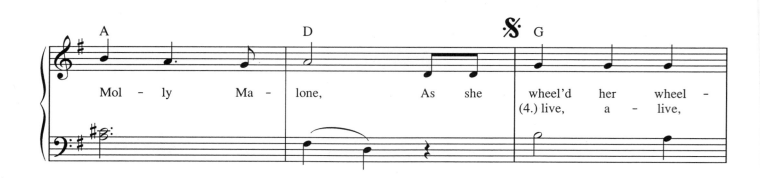

Mol - ly Ma - lone, As she wheel'd her wheel -
(4.) live, a - live,

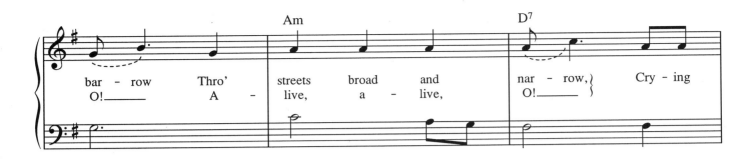

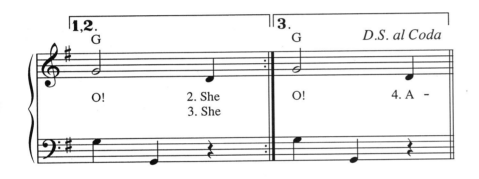

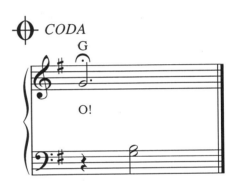

Verse 2:

She was a fishmonger,
But sure t'was no wonder,
For so were her father and mother before,
And they each wheel'd their barrow
Thro' streets broad and narrow
Crying cockles and mussels! Alive, alive, O!

Verse 3:

She died of a fever,
And no one could save her,
And that was the end of sweet Molly Malone,
But her ghost wheels her barrow
Thro' streets broad and narrow
Crying cockles and mussels! Alive, alive, O!

Danny Boy

Traditional Irish Melody
Words by Fred E. Weatherly

Moderately

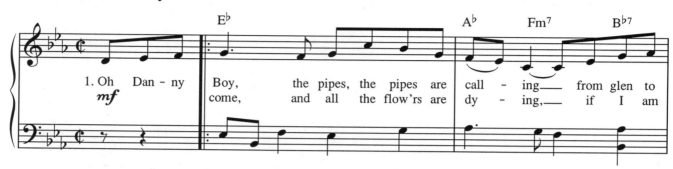

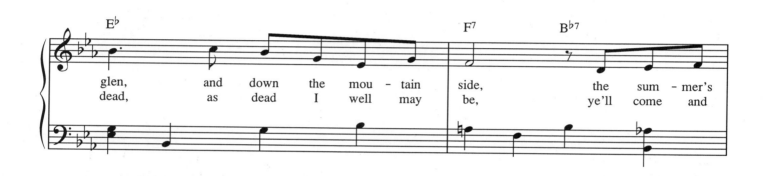

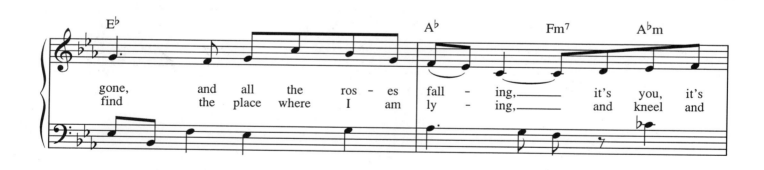

mea - dow,_____ or when the val - ley's hushed and white with
bove__ me,_____ and all my grave will warm - er, sweet - er

snow, and you'll be here in sun - shine or in
be, for you will bend and tell me that you

sha - dow,_____ oh Dan - ny Boy, oh Dan - ny Boy, I love you
love__ me,_____ and I shall sleep in peace un - til you come to

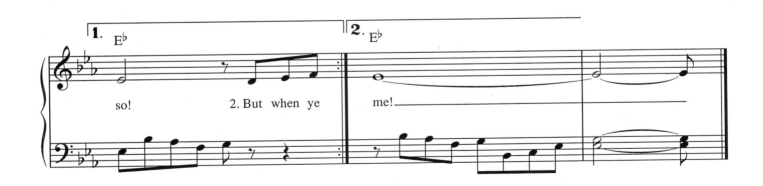

1. so! 2. But when ye

2. me!_____

Galway Bay

Words & Music by Dr Arthur Colahan

Moderately slow

If you | ev - er go a-cross the sea to | Ire - land, | then

breez - es blow - ing o'er the seas from | Ire - land, | are

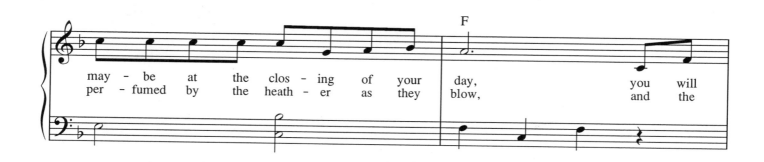

may - be at the clos - ing of your | day, | you will

per - fumed by the heath - er as they | blow, | and the

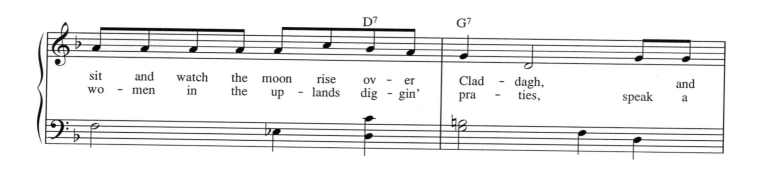

sit and watch the moon rise ov - er | Clad - dagh, | and

wo - men in the up - lands dig - gin' | pra - ties, | speak a

see the sun go down on Gal - way | Bay. | Just to

lan - guage that the strang - ers do not | know. | For the

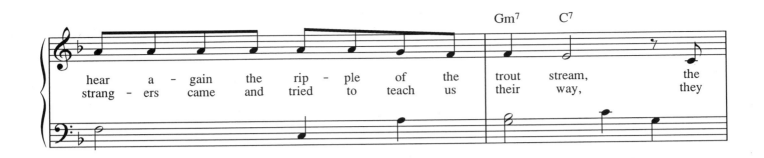

hear a - gain the rip - ple of the trout stream, the
strang - ers came and tried to of teach us their way, they

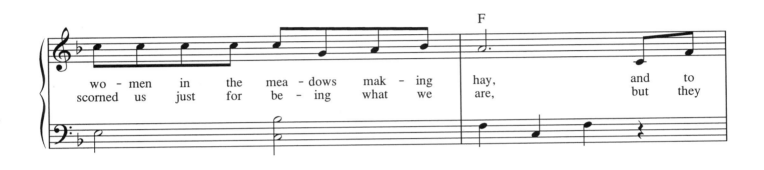

wo - men in the mea - dows mak - ing hay, and to
scorned us just for be - ing what we are, but they

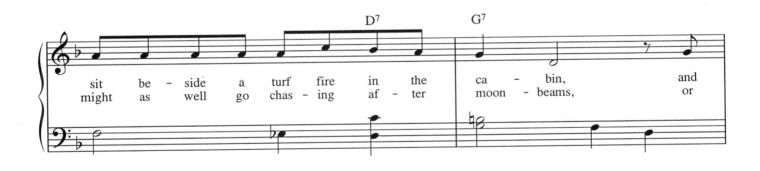

sit be - side a turf fire in the ca - bin, and
might as well go chas - ing af - ter moon - beams, or

watch the bare - foot Gos - soons at their play. For the
light a pen - ny can - dle from a

13

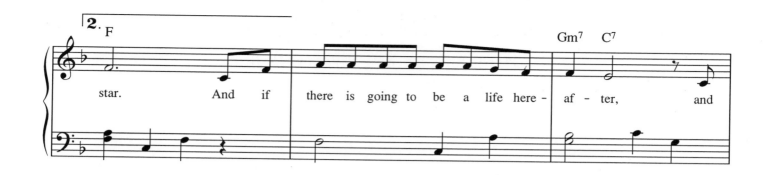

star.   And if   there is going to be a life here - af - ter,   and

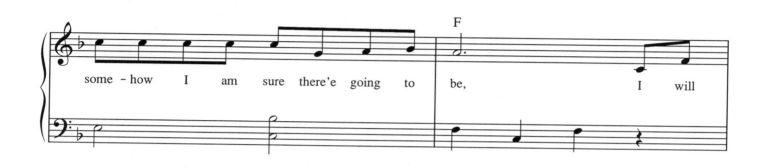

some - how I am sure there'e going to be,   I will

ask my God to let me make my hea - ven,   in

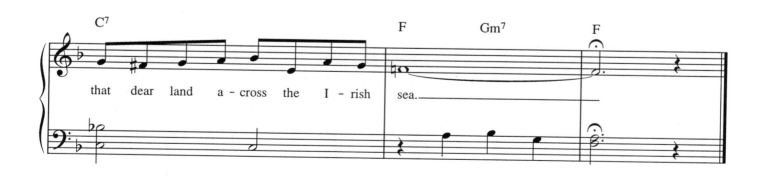

that dear land a - cross the I - rish sea.___

My Wild Irish Rose

Words & Music by Chauncey Olcott

Moderately

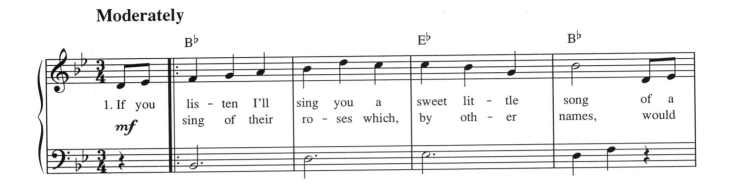

1. If you lis - ten I'll sing you a sweet lit - tle song of a
sing of their ro - ses which, by oth - er names, would

flow - er that's now drooped and dead,＿ yet＿ dear - er to me, yes, than
smell just as sweet - ly, they say,＿ but I know that my Rose＿ would

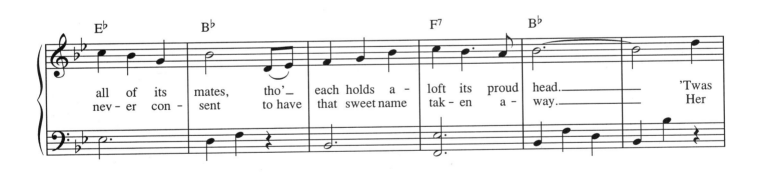

all of its mates, tho'＿ each holds a - loft its proud head.＿ 'Twas
nev - er con - sent to have that sweet name tak - en a - way.＿ Her

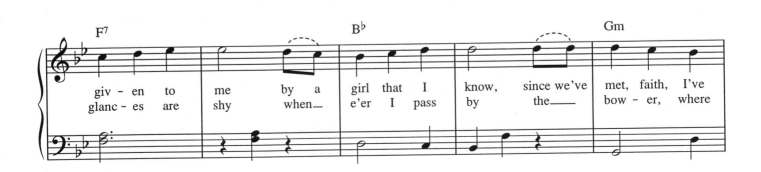

giv - en to me by a girl that I know, since we've met, faith, I've
glanc - es are shy when＿ e'er I pass by the＿ bow - er, where

Ir - ish Rose._____ My wild

Ir - ish Rose,_____ the dear - est

flower that grows_____ and some day for my

sake, she may let me take the bloom from my

wild Ir - ish Rose._____ 2. They may Rose._____

17

I'll Take You Home Again Kathleen

Words & Music by Thomas P. Westendorf

Slow

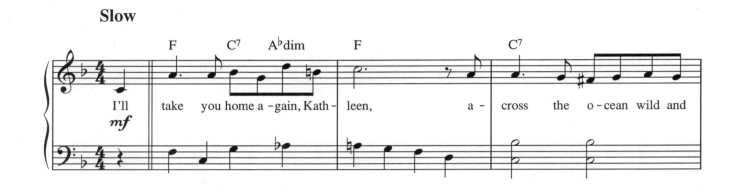

I'll take you home a-gain, Kath-leen, a-cross the o-cean wild and

wide, to where your heart has ev-er been, since

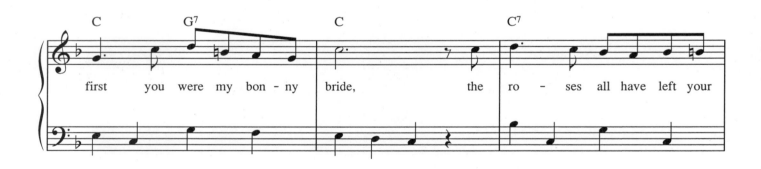

first you were my bon-ny bride, the ro-ses all have left your

cheek, I've watched them fade a-way and die; your

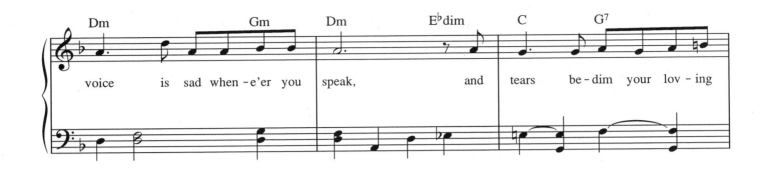

voice is sad when-e'er you speak, and tears be-dim your lov-ing

eyes. Oh, I will take you back, Kath- leen, to

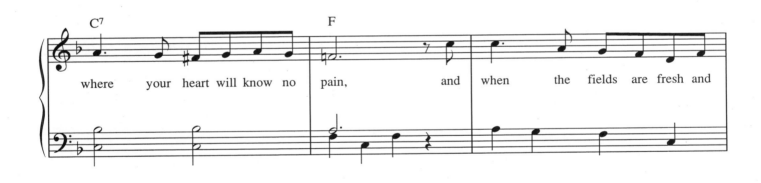

where your heart will know no pain, and when the fields are fresh and

green, I'll— take you to your home a- gain.—

If You're Irish Come Into The Parlour

Words & Music by Shaun Glenville & Frank Miller

If You Ever Go To Ireland

Words and Music by Art Noel

Moderately

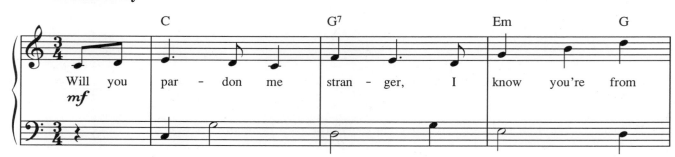

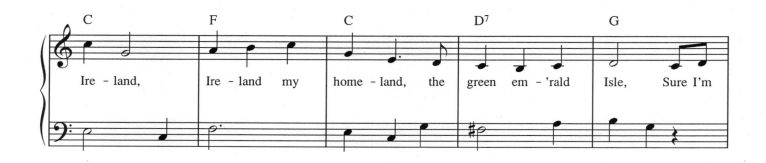

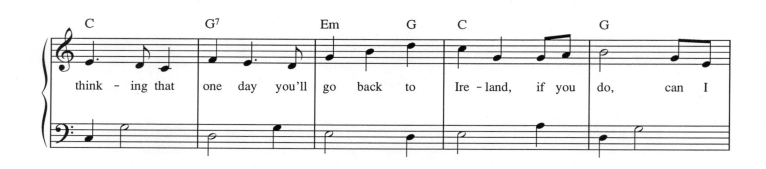

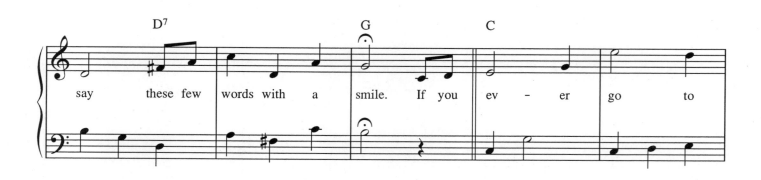

Irish Eyes

Words & Music by Hank Locklin & George Carroll

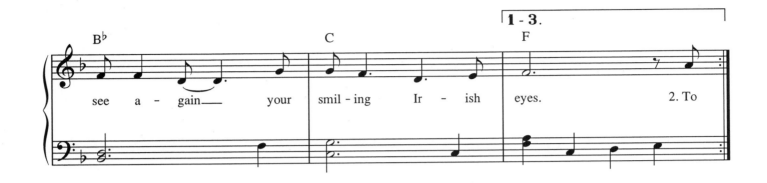

see a - gain___ your smil - ing Ir - ish eyes. 2. To

eyes. I love you and I need__ you__ my love - ly Ir - ish eyes.

Verse 2:

To stroll again Antrim's Glens and see the waterfall
To sleep beneath the mystic hills in dear old Donegal
Or walk the shores of Eireann and hear the seagulls cry
But most of all to look into your lovely Irish eyes.

Verse 3:

To hear again those Shandon bells ringing heavenly
Beside the laughing waters of the lovely Lee
Or listen to the ocean and the wind that sighs
But most of all to see again your smiling Irish eyes.

Verse 4:

In dreams I see your angel face that aches my lonely heart
The memory when I told you we would have to part
I can't forget that morning when we said goodbye
I can't forget those teardrops in your Irish eyes.
I love you and I need you, my lovely Irish eyes.

It's A Long Way To Tipperary

Words & Music by Jack Judge & Harry Williams

Moderately bright

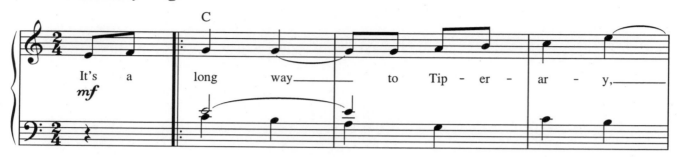

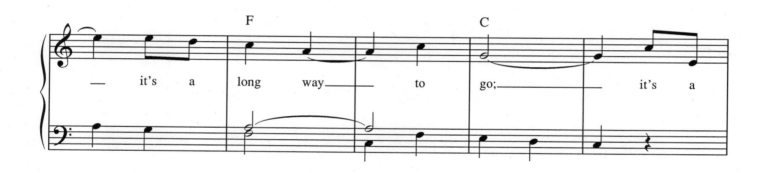

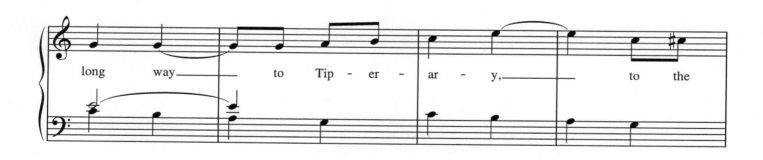

Patsy Fagan (The Dacent Irish Boy)

Words & Music by Thomas P. Keenan

Moderately bright

1. I'm work-in' here in Glas-gow, I've got a da-cent job, *(Verses 2 & 3 see block lyric)*

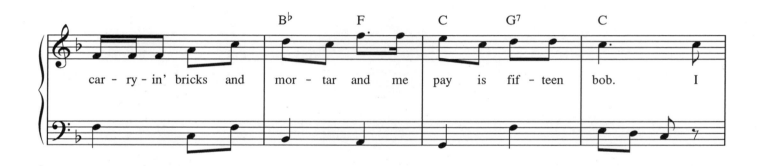

car-ry-in' bricks and mor-tar and me pay is fif-teen bob. I

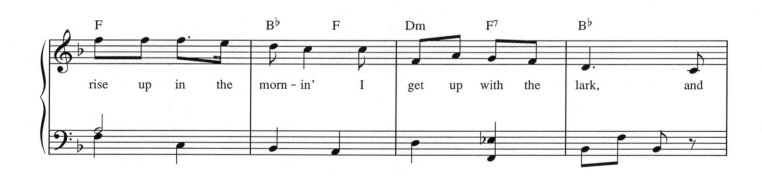

rise up in the morn-in' I get up with the lark, and

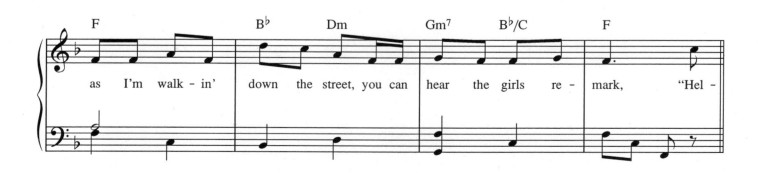

as I'm walk-in' down the street, you can hear the girls re-mark, "Hel-

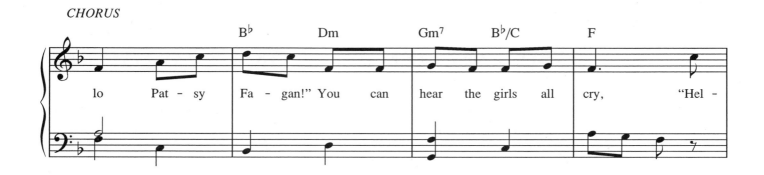

lo Pat - sy Fa - gan!" You can hear the girls all cry, "Hel -

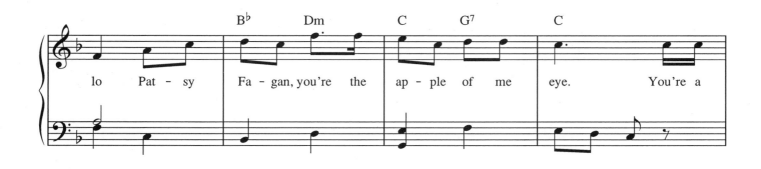

lo Pat - sy Fa - gan, you're the ap - ple of me eye. You're a

da - cent boy from Ire - land, there's no one can de - ny, You're a

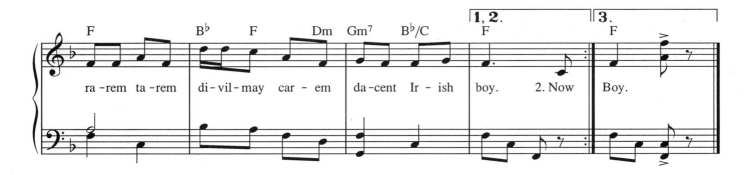

ra - rem ta - rem di - vil - may car - em da - cent Ir - ish boy. 2. Now Boy.

Verse 2:

Now if there's one among you
Would like to marry me
I'll take her to a little home
Across the Irish sea.
I'll dress her up in satin
And please her all I can
And let her people see that I'm
A dacent Irishman.

Verse 3:

The day that I left Ireland,
'Twas many years ago
I left me home in Antrim
Where the pigs and praties grow.
But since I left old Ireland
It's always been my plan
To let the people see that I'm
A dacent Irishman.

Rose Of Tralee

Words & Music by E.M. Spencer & C.W. Glover

Moderately

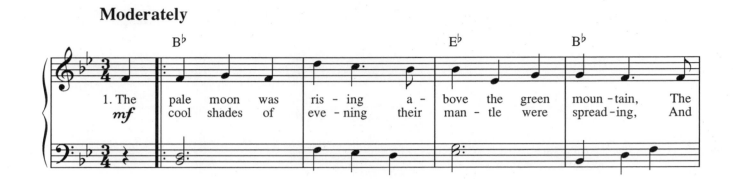

1. The pale moon was ris-ing a-bove the green moun-tain, The
cool shades of eve-ning their man-tle were spread-ing, And

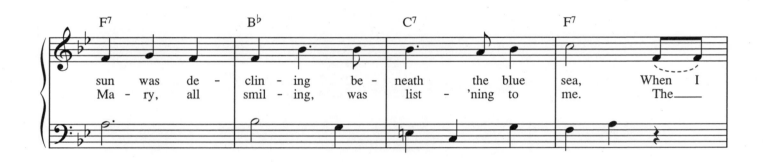

sun was de-clin-ing be-neath the blue sea, When I
Ma-ry, all smil-ing, was list-'ning to me. The

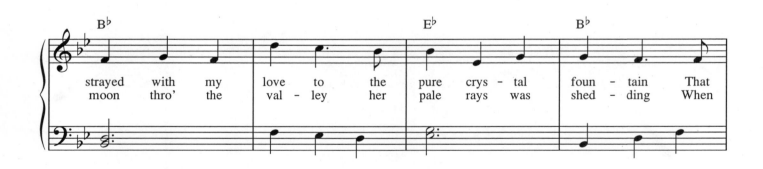

strayed with my love to the pure crys-tal foun-tain That
moon thro' the val-ley her pale rays was shed-ding When

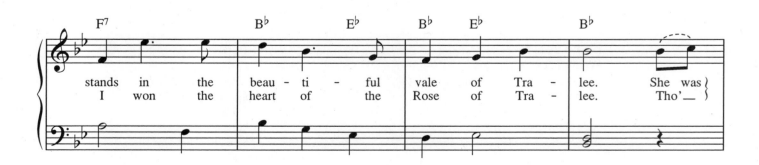

stands in the beau-ti-ful vale of Tra-lee. She was
I won the heart of the Rose of Tra-lee. Tho'

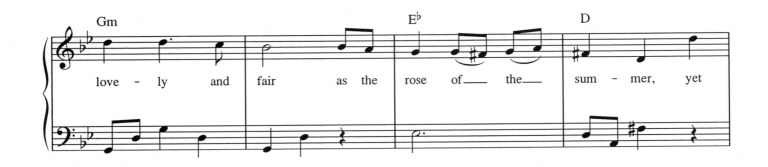

love - ly and fair as the rose of___ the___ sum - mer, yet

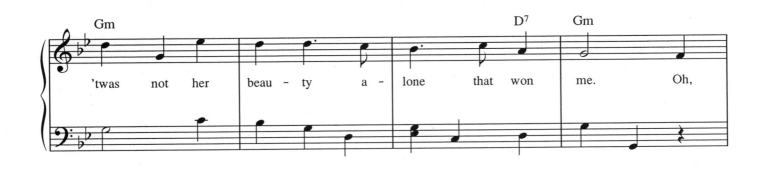

'twas not her beau - ty a - lone that won me. Oh,

no! 'Twas the truth in her eyes ev - er dawn - ing That

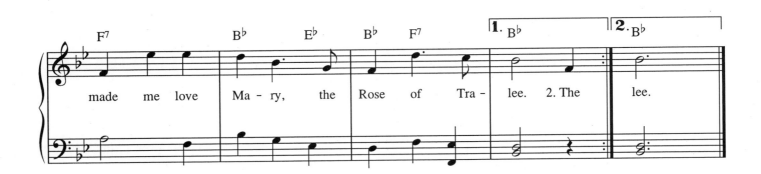

made me love Ma - ry, the Rose of Tra - lee. 2. The lee.

The Black Velvet Band

Irish Traditional

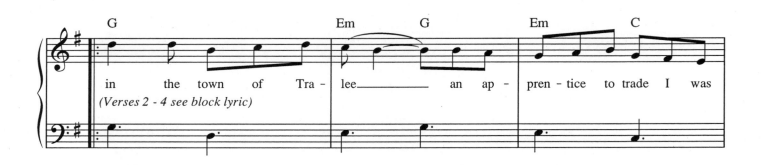

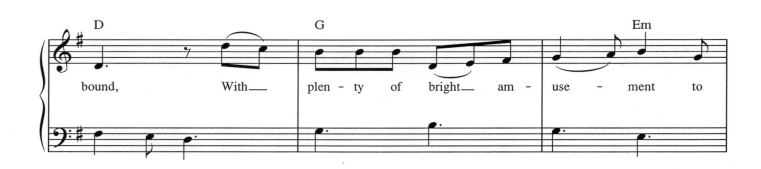

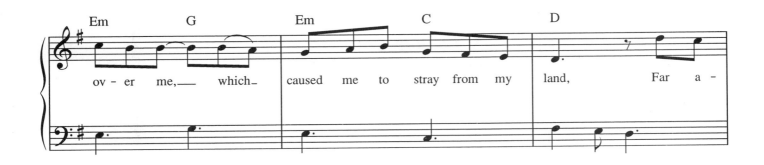

over me,— which— caused me to stray from my land, Far a-

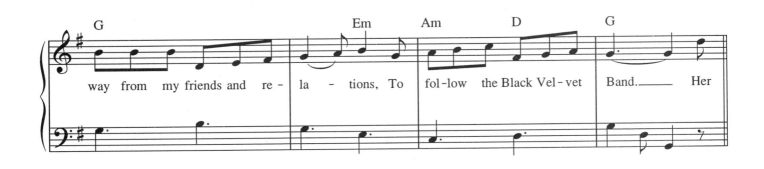

way from my friends and re - la - tions, To fol-low the Black Vel-vet Band.— Her

CHORUS

eyes they shone— like dia - monds,— you'd— think she was queen of the

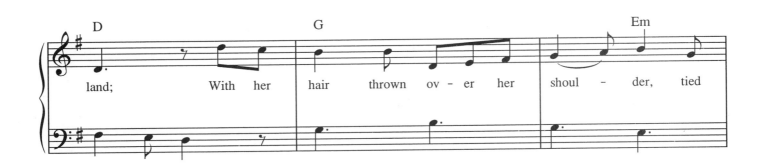

land; With her hair thrown ov - er her shoul - der, tied

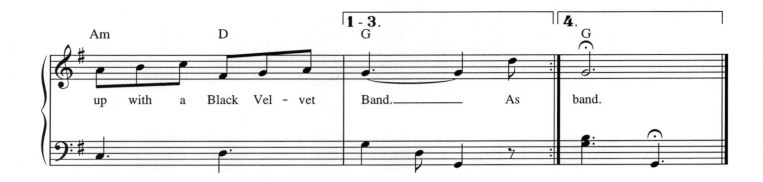

up with a Black Vel - vet Band._____ As band.

Verse 2:

As I went walking down Broadway, not intending to stay very long,
I met with a frolicsome damsel, as she came tripping along.
A watch she pulled out of her pocket and slipped it right into my hand;
On the very first day that I met her, bad luck to the Black Velvet Band.

Verse 3:

Before the judge and the jury the both of us had to appear,
And a gentleman swore to the jewellery - the case against us was clear,
For seven years transportation right unto Van Dieman's Land
Far away from my friends and relations, to follow her Black Velvet Band.

Verse 4:

Oh all you brave young Irish lads, a warning take by me
Beware of the pretty young damsels that are knocking around in Tralee
They'll treat you to whiskey and porter, until you're unable to stand
And before you have time for to leave them, you are unto Van Dieman's Land.

The Mountains Of Mourne

Traditional

Moderately

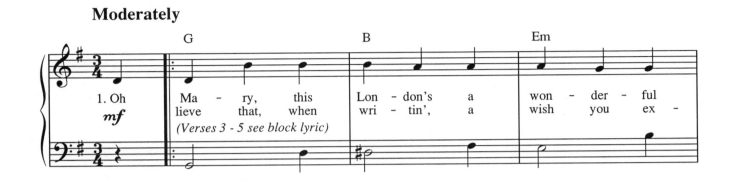

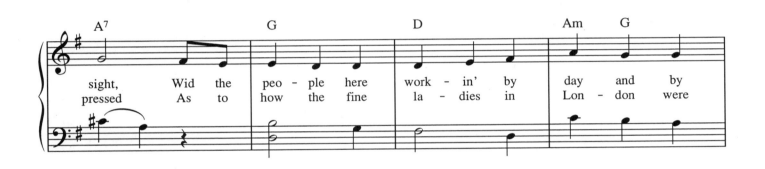

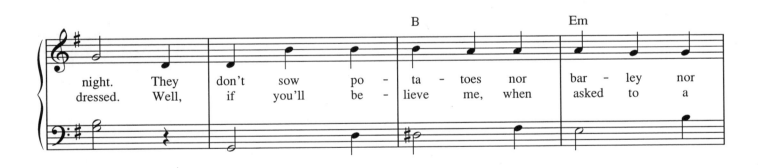

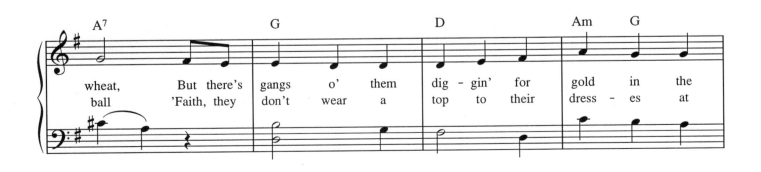

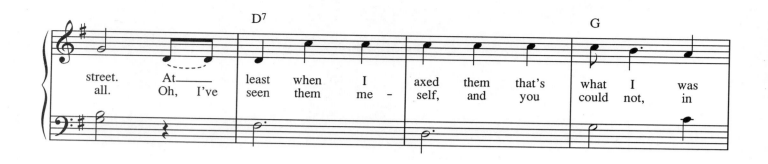

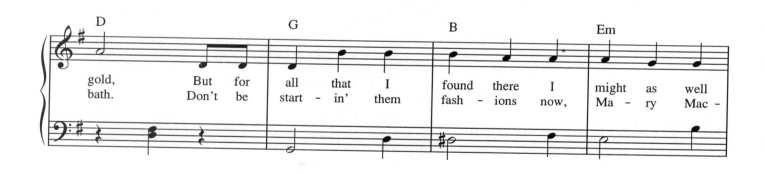

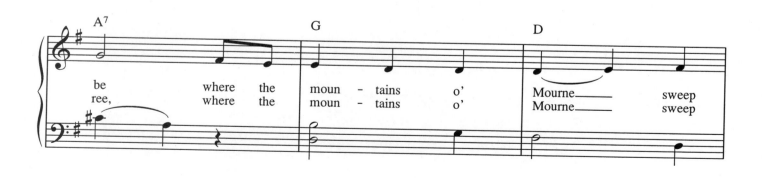

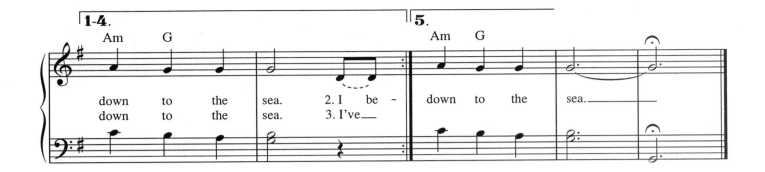

Verse 3:

I've seen England's King from the top of a bus;
I never knew him, tho' he means to know us.
And, tho' by the Saxon we once were oppressed,
Still I cheered (God forgive me!), I cheered with the rest.
And, now that he's visited Erin's green shore,
We'll be much better friends than we've been heretofore.
When we've got all we want, we're as quiet as can be
Where the mountains of Mourne sweep down to the sea.

Verse 4:

You remember young Peter O'Loughlin, of course?
Well, now he is here at the head of the force.
I met him today, I was crossin' the Strand,
And he stopped the whole street wid wan wave of his hand.
And there we stood talkin' of days that are gone,
While the whole population of London looked on.
But, for all these great powers, he's wishful, like me,
To be back where dark Mourne sweeps down to the sea.

Verse 5:

There's beautiful girls here - oh, nivver you mind! -
Wid beautiful shapes nature niver designed,
And lovely complexions, all roses and crame;
But O'Loughlin remarked, wid regard to the same,
That "If those roses you venture to sip,
The colours might all come away on your lip."
So I'll wait for the wild rose that's waitin' for me
Where the mountains of Mourne sweep down to the sea.

The Irish Rover

Adapted by Pat Clancy, Tom Clancy, Liam Clancy & Tommy Makem

Moderately bright

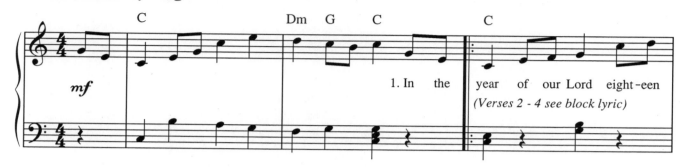

1. In the year of our Lord eight-een
(Verses 2 - 4 see block lyric)

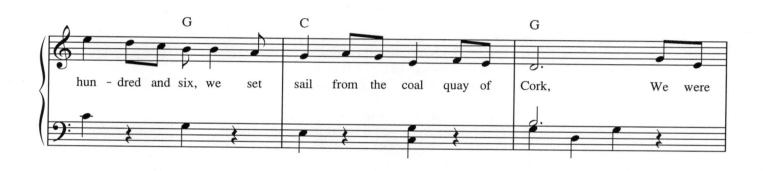

hun - dred and six, we set sail from the coal quay of Cork, We were

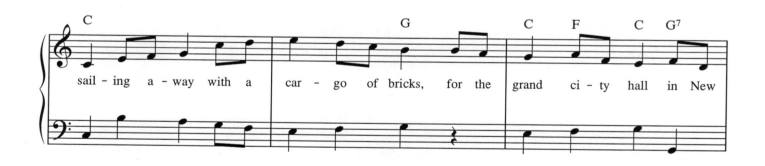

sail - ing a - way with a car - go of bricks, for the grand ci - ty hall in New

York. We'd an e - le - gant craft, it was rigged fore and aft, and

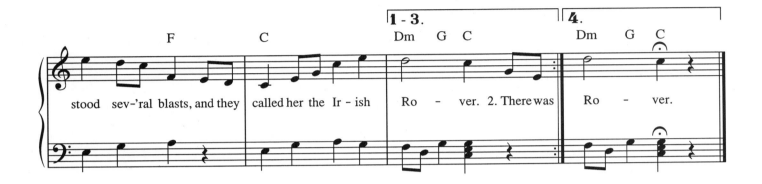

Verse 2:

There was Barney Magee, from the banks of the Lee
There was Hogan, from County Tyrone
There was Johnny McGurk, who was scared stiff of work
And a chap from Westmeath named Malone.
There was Slugger O'Toole, who was drunk as a rule
And fighting Bill Tracy from Dover.
And your man Mick McCann from the banks of the Bann
Was the skipper on the Irish Rover.

Verse 3:

We had one million bags of the best Sligo rags
We had two million barrels of bone
We three million bales of old nanny goats' tails
We had four million barrels of stone.
We had five million hogs and six million dogs
And seven million barrels of porter.
We had eight million sides of old blind horses' hides
In the hold of the Irish Rover.

Verse 4:

We had sailed seven years when the measles broke out,
And our ship lost her way in a fog
And the whole of the crew was reduced down to two
'Twas myself and the captain's old dog.
Then the ship struck a rock, O Lord, what a shock
And near tumbled over
Turned nine times around, then the poor old dog was drowned.
I'm the last of the Irish Rover.

The Spinning Wheel

Words & Music by John Francis Waller & Delia Murphy

Moderately slow

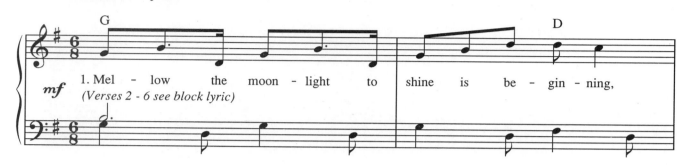

1. Mel - low the moon - light to shine is be - gin - ning,
(Verses 2 - 6 see block lyric)

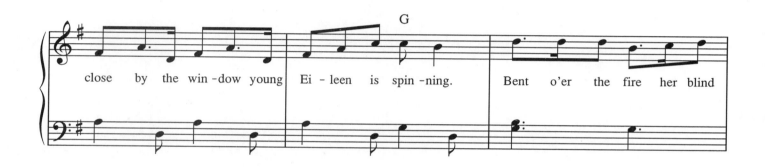

close by the win - dow young Ei - leen is spin - ning. Bent o'er the fire her blind

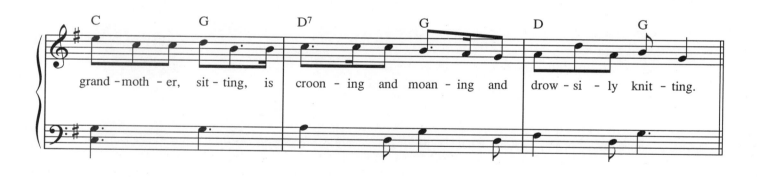

grand - moth - er, sit - ting, is croon - ing and moan - ing and drow - si - ly knit - ting.

CHORUS

Mer - ri - ly, cheer - i - ly, nois - i - ly whirr - ing, swing the wheel, spins the wheel

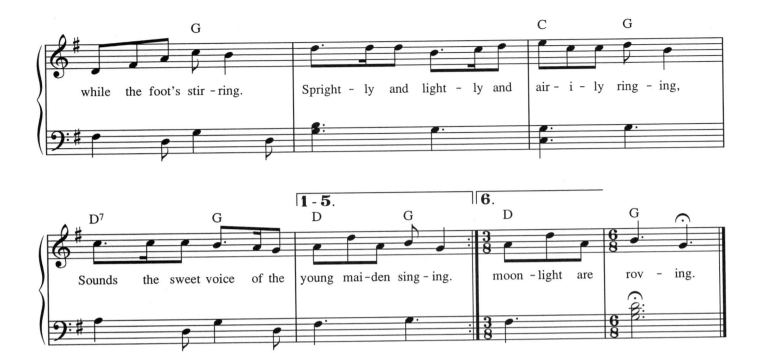

Verse 2:

"Eileen, a chara, I hear someone tapping,"
"'Tis the ivy, dear mother, against the glass flapping."
"Eily, I surely hear somebody sighing,"
"'Tis the sound, mother dear, of the autumn winds dying."

Verse 3:

"What's that noise that I hear at the window I wonder?"
"'Tis the little birds chirping the holly-bush under"
"What makes you be pushing and moving your stool on?"
"And singing all wrong the old song of Coolin?"

Verse 4:

There's a form at the casement, the form of her true love,
And he whispers with face bent, "I'm waiting for you, love"
"Get up on the stool, through the lattice step lightly,
And we'll rove in the grove whilst the moon's shining brightly."

Verse 5:

The maid shakes her head, on her lips lays her fingers,
Steals up from the seat, longs to go and yet lingers,
A frightened glance turns to her drowsy grandmother,
Puts one foot on the stool, spins the wheel with the other.

Verse 6:

Lazily, easily, swings now the wheel round,
Slowly and lowly is heard now the reel's sound,
Noiseless and light to the lattice above her
The maid steps, then leaps to the arms of her lover.

Final Chorus:

Slower, and slower, and slower the wheel swings,
Lower, and lower, and lower the reel rings,
Ere the reel and the wheel stopped their spinning and moving,
Through the grove the young lovers by moonlight are roving.

When Irish Eyes Are Smiling

Words by George Graff & Chauncey Olcott
Music by Ernest Ball

Whistling Gypsy (The Gypsy Rover)

Words & Music by Leo Maguire

Moderately

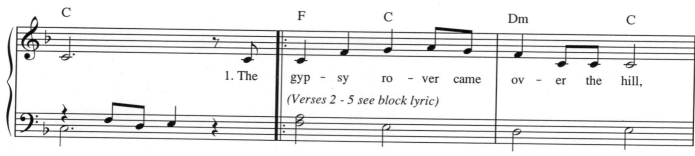

1. The gyp - sy ro - ver came ov - er the hill,
(Verses 2 - 5 see block lyric)

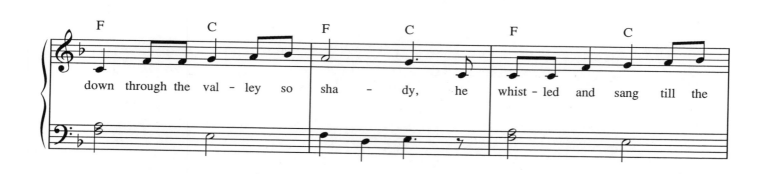

down through the val - ley so sha - dy, he whist - led and sang till the

green-woods rang, and he won the heart of a la - dy.

CHORUS

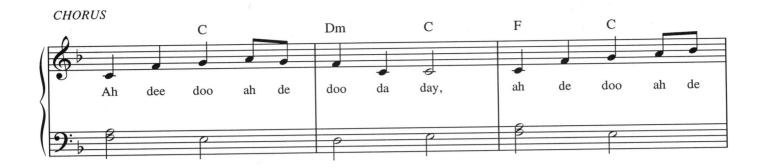

Ah dee doo ah de doo da day, ah de doo ah de

day de, he whist – led and sang till the green – woods rang, and

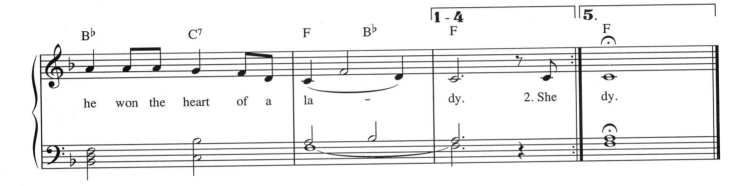

he won the heart of a la – dy. 2. She dy.

Verse 2:

She left her father's castle gate
She left her fair young lover
She left her servants and her state
To follow the gypsy rover.

Verse 3:

Her father saddled up his fastest steed
He ranged the valleys over
He sought his daughter at great speed
And the whistling gypsy rover.

Verse 4:

He came at last to a mansion fine
Down by the river Clady
And there was music and there was wine
For the gypsy and his lady.

Verse 5:

"He is no gypsy, father dear,
But lord of these lands all over
I'm going to stay 'til my dying day
With my whistling gypsy rover."

The Wild Colonial Boy

Words & Music by Joseph M. Crofts

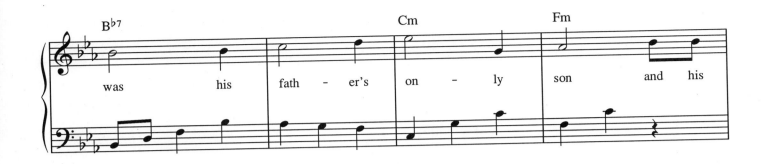

was   his   fath - er's   on - ly   son   and   his

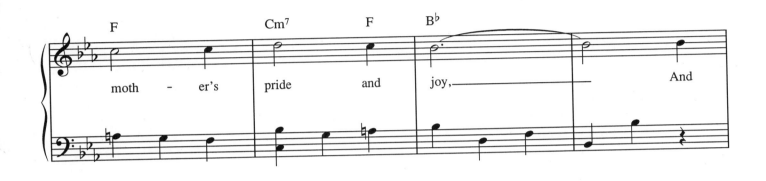

moth - er's   pride   and   joy,_____ And

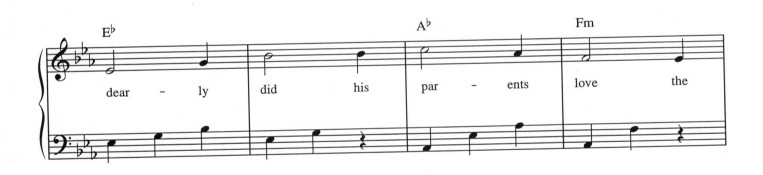

dear - ly   did   his   par - ents   love   the

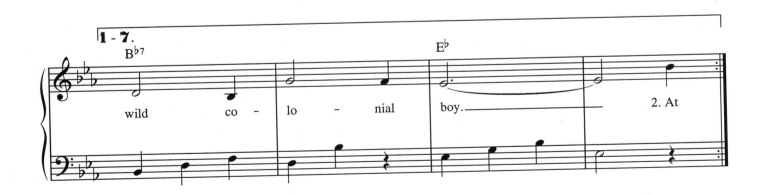

wild   co - lo - nial   boy._____ 2. At

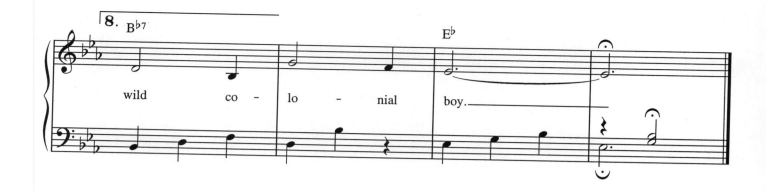

8. Bb7 ... Eb

wild co - lo - nial boy.____

Verse 2:

At hammer throwing Jack was great
Or swinging a Caman
He led the boys in all their pranks
Fron dusk to early dawn.
At fishin' or at poachin' trout
He was the rale "McCoy"
And all the neighbours loved young Jack
The wild colonial boy.

Verse 3:

At the early age of sixteen years
He left his native home
And to Australia's sunny land
He was inclined to roam.
He robbed the rich, and he helped the poor
He stabbed James MacEvoy
A terror to Australia was
The wild colonial boy.

Verse 4:

For two more years this daring youth
Ran on his wild career
With a head that knew no danger
And a heart that knew no fear.
He robbed outright the wealthy squires
And their arms he did destroy
And woe to all who dared to fight
The wild colonial boy.

Verse 5:

He loved the Prairie and the Bush
Where rangers rode along
With his gun stuck in its holster deep
He sang a merry song.
But if a foe once crossed his track
And sought him to destroy
He'd get sharp shootin' sure from Jack
The wild colonial boy.

Verse 6:

One morning on the Prairie wild
Jack Duggan rode along
Whilst listening to the mocking bird
Singing a cheerful song.
Out jumped three troupers, fierce and grim
Kelly, Davis and Fitzroy
They all set out to capture him
The wild colonial boy.

Verse 7:

"Surrender now, Jack Duggan, come!
You see there's three to one!
Surrender in the Queen's name, sir!
You, are a plundering son!"
Jack drew two pistols from his side
And glared upon Fitzroy,
"I'll fight, but not surrender!" cried
The wild colonial boy.

Verse 8:

He fired a shot at Kelly
Which brought him to the ground
He fired point blank at Davis, too
Who fell dead at the sound.
But a bullet pierced his brave young heart
From the pistol of Fitzroy
And that was how they captured him
The wild colonial boy.